Gross and Yucky
Human Body

Interactive Quiz

Managing Editors: Simon Melhuish and Sarah Wells
Series Editor: Nikole G Bamford
Designer: Linley J Clode
Writer: Paul Lucas

Published by
The Lagoon Group
PO Box 311, KT2 5QW, UK
PO Box 990676, Boston, MA 02199, USA

ISBN: 1904797105

www.intelliquestbooks.com

Printed in China

IntelliQuest

UNIQUE BOOK CODE	026

Instructions

First of all make sure you have a Quizmo –

Find the book's unique code (this appears at the top of this page). Use the < and > buttons to scroll to this number on the Quizmo screen. Press the ⏎ button to enter the code, and you're ready to go.

Use the < > scroll buttons to select the question number you want to answer. Press the **A**, **B**, **C**, or **D** button to enter your chosen answer.

If you are correct the green light beside the button you pressed will flash. You can then use the scroll button to move on to another question.

If your answer is incorrect, the red light beside the button you pressed will flash.

Don't worry, you can try again and again until you have the correct answer, OR move on to another question. (Beware: the more times you guess incorrectly, the lower your final percentage score will be!)

You can finish the quiz at any point – just press the ◆ button to find out your score and rank as follows:

75% or above	Hey there superbrain! You sure know your body parts!
50% – 74%	You're a human body brainbox!
25% – 49%	You're obviously not into all that icky stuff...
Less than 25%	Are you actually human...?

If you do press the ◆ button to find out your score, this will end your session and you will have to use the ◆ to start again!

HAVE FUN!

001

If you are "steatopygous" what do you have?

    A) A big nose
    B) A hairy behind
    C) A hairy nose
    D) A big behind

002

If it was laid out flat, how much space would a fully grown man's skin take up?

    A) As much space as a washcloth
    B) As much space as a single bed
    C) As much space as a hand towel
    D) As much space as a double bed

003

What percentage of house dust is made up of dead human skin?

    A) 1%
    B) 10%
    C) 50%
    D) 99%

How many people in the world are known to have the rarest blood group, group A-H?

A) One old woman in Skegness
B) About half a million
C) About two thousand
D) About ten

By what age would you probably be dead if you'd been born in Fifth Century England?

A) 30 years old
B) 35 years old
C) 40 years old
D) 70 years old

Which fingernail grows the fastest?

A) The thumbnail
B) The index finger nail
C) The little finger nail
D) The middle finger nail

004

005

006

007 **W**hich fingernail grows the slowest?

- **A)** The thumbnail
- **B)** The index finger nail
- **C)** The middle finger nail
- **D)** The little finger nail

008 **H**ow fast can a sneeze travel?

- **A)** 5mph/8kph
- **B)** 30mph/48kph
- **C)** 100mph/161kph
- **D)** 50mph/80kph

009 **H**ow much spit does the body make every day?

- **A)** About a bucket full
- **B)** About a teacup full
- **C)** About an eggcup full
- **D)** About a lunchbox full

Which of these did The Romans use as toothpaste?

A) Mucus
B) Pee
C) Blood
D) Ear wax

Talalgia is a pain in the what?

A) Ankle
B) Neck
C) Elbow
D) Behind

Whereabouts is the biggest muscle in the body?

A) The jaw
B) The behind
C) The chest
D) The arm

What percentage of your blood could you spurt out without dying?

A) 1%
B) 10%
C) 30%
D) 90%

The average human body has enough fat to make how many bars of soap?

A) 7
B) 2
C) 9
D) 13

Saint Apollonia is the patron saint of what?

A) Spots
B) Dandruff
C) Toothache
D) Slime

If you suffered from blepharospasms, what would you be unable to stop doing?

- **A)** Farting
- **B)** Laughing
- **C)** Burping
- **D)** Winking

Which of these gases does NOT emerge in a fart?

- **A)** Methane
- **B)** Oxygen
- **C)** Nitrogen
- **D)** Sulfur

Which of these is NOT a part of dandruff?

- **A)** Oil
- **B)** Dirt
- **C)** Head lice
- **D)** Dead skin cells

019

Comedones is another name for what?

A) Sweaty feet
B) Boils
C) Nose hair
D) Blackheads

020

Attila The Hun was a bloodthirsty warlord in 450 A.D. – what did he die of?

A) A nosebleed
B) A smashed skull
C) A cut throat
D) A splinter

021

How many different functions does the liver perform?

A) The odd 1 or 2
B) 50
C) 200
D) 500

Indole and Skatole are two chemicals responsible for what?

A) Making poop smell
B) Making puke green
C) Making pus yellow
D) Making snot runny

How long after you've eaten can food still be in the stomach?

A) A month
B) A week
C) 8 hours
D) 4 hours

Which of these does the stomach produce?

A) Hydrochloric acid
B) Sulfuric acid
C) Lactic acid
D) Citric acid

025 About what size is the pituitary gland?

A) The size of a baked bean
B) The size of a boiled egg
C) The size of a boiled head
D) The size of a baked head

026 Which of these is the medical term for that feeling when your hair stands on end?

A) Scariosis
B) Horripilation
C) Creepisilation
D) Heebeegeebeeoscomy

027 About how long is the alimentary canal?

A) 9cm/3.5in
B) 90m/295ft
C) 9m/29.5ft
D) 9km/5.5m

What does borborygmy describe?

    A) The sound of a tummy rumbling
    B) The sound of an old man farting
    C) The sound of a tickly cough
    D) The sound of puking

028

How long does it take for the body to grow an entire new layer of skin?

    A) 6 seconds
    B) A week
    C) A month
    D) 30 years

028

If you were to suffer from "The Bends" what would happen to you?

    A) Your face would melt
    B) Your eyeballs would burst
    C) Your spine would rot
    D) Your blood would bubble

030

What speed can a cough travel at?
- **A)** 500mph/805kph
- **B)** 100mph/161kph
- **C)** 60mph/97kph
- **D)** 1000mph/1609kph

What function does nose hair perform?
- **A)** Manufactures mucus
- **B)** Cleans and warms air
- **C)** Protects you from fart smells
- **D)** Stops bees from flying into your brain

How much does an eyeball weigh?
- **A)** About 3 grams/0.106 ounces
- **B)** About 10 grams/0.353 ounces
- **C)** About 30 grams/1 ounce
- **D)** About 100 grams/3.5 ounces

W hat's special about the Hyoid bone?

034

A) It's the thinnest bone in the body
B) It's the only bone in the body that isn't connected to any other bone
C) It's the only bone in the body that's floppy
D) It's the only bone in the body that's hairy

H ow many pencils could you make from the carbon in a human body?

035

A) 1
B) 9
C) 90
D) 900

W hich of these are babies born without?

036

A) Brains
B) Kneecaps
C) Butts
D) Ankles

037

About what age do your eyes stop growing?
- **A)** At about 7 or 8 years
- **B)** At birth
- **C)** At about 18 years
- **D)** They never stop growing

038

About how much digestive juice does the human body make every day?
- **A)** 2 gallons/9 litres
- **B)** 64 ounces/2 litres
- **C)** 3 gallons/23 litres
- **D)** 32 ounces/1 litres

039

What is deglutition?
- **A)** Blowing your nose
- **B)** Spitting
- **C)** Swallowing
- **D)** Peeing

How fast does pain travel?

A) About 1.25in/3cm an hour
B) About 186 miles/300km an hour
C) About 984ft/300m an hour
D) About 10ft/3m an hour

The first operation performed using an anesthetic was in 1846. What did it involve?

A) Taking out a hat-maker's appendix
B) Cutting off a soldier's arm
C) Taking out a sailor's brains
D) Cutting off a butler's leg

If it had enough food, how long would it take a single bacterium to reproduce into a ball of bacteria the size of the earth?

A) 3 hours
B) 3 days
C) 3 weeks
D) 3 months

043

The word "vaccination" comes from the Latin word for what?

- **A)** Nipple
- **B)** Blood
- **C)** Banana
- **D)** Cow

044

In 1996, a teenager in New York met which of these sticky ends?

- **A)** He was mauled to death by his pet rabbit
- **B)** He was poisoned by his pet tarantula
- **C)** He was crushed to death by his pet snake
- **D)** He was eaten by his pet guinea pig

045

What's the body's largest organ?

- **A)** Heart
- **B)** Skin
- **C)** Kidney
- **D)** Liver

What is the headache tablet "aspirin" made from?

- **A)** Seaweed
- **B)** Mud
- **C)** Fish eyes
- **D)** Tree bark

046

How often is the fluid inside your eyeballs replaced?

- **A)** 16 times a day
- **B)** 16 times a year
- **C)** Depends how often your eyeballs can be bothered
- **D)** Never

047

Oxygen in your blood makes it appear red, but what color is it really?

- **A)** Green
- **B)** Golden
- **C)** Blue
- **D)** White

048

049

At what speed does your body move food along from your mouth to your behind?

    A) 8ft/2.5m per second
    B) 8ft/2.5m per hour
    C) 8ft/2.5m per day
    D) 8ft/2.5m per week

050

Bone is regularly renewed by your body. How long does it take your body to make the equivalent of a whole new skeleton?

    A) A day
    B) A month
    C) A year
    D) 7 years

051

Which of these did the Ancient Egyptians use as eyewash?

    A) Donkey slobber
    B) Leopard blood
    C) Crocodile poop
    D) Elephant pee

What does the brain have to do to the image your eyes see to make it appear normal?

    A) Wiggle it from side to side
    B) Turn it upside down
    C) Add the color orange to it
    D) Chop it up into pieces

052

What are ganglia?

    A) Long thin bogeys
    B) Bunches of nerve cells
    C) Bunches of nervous cells
    D) Long thin blood vessels

053

What shape is the stomach?

    A) Letter "O" shaped
    B) Letter "G" shaped
    C) Letter "J" shaped
    D) Letter "Z" shaped

054

055 How many different faces can the face muscles pull?

    A) About a hundred
    B) About a thousand
    C) About three thousand
    D) About seven thousand

056 Tycho Brahe was a famous Danish astronomer. Which of these gory deaths do you think he suffered?

    A) His behind exploded from needing a poo
    B) He puked so hard his lungs came out
    C) He farted so hard he exploded
    D) His bladder burst from needing to pee

057 What is "chyme?"

    A) A sort of loaf made of earwax
    B) A sort of soup made of partly digested food
    C) A sort of cake made of pus
    D) A sort of pie made of poop

If you pulled out all your internal organs and dropped them in the bath, which of them would float?

058

A) Your kidneys
B) Your brains
C) Your heart
D) Your lungs

What shape is the eyeball of a near-sighted person?

059

A) Egg-shaped
B) Round
C) Banana-shaped
D) Square

DNA stands for what?

060

A) Dads Never Argue
B) Dreaded Nocturnal Acne
C) Deacronyminous Acid
D) Deoxyribonucleic Acid

061

In the Malay language, the term "buang air besar" is used to describe having a poop. What does it literally mean in English?

A) To make a smelly snake
B) To spin brown thread
C) To throw big water
D) To talk with the other mouth

062

Where are the fastest reacting muscles in the body to be found?

A) In the eye
B) In the behind
C) In the nose
D) In the fingers

063

When you "crack" your knuckles or click your ankle, the sound you hear is due to what?

A) Bubbles of nitrogen popping
B) Chunks of bones splitting
C) Lumps of gristle snapping
D) Clumps of blood vessels bursting

Say you've got gangrene and your leg is rotting off. What would it smell of?

A) Chicken curry
B) Moldy apples
C) Two-week-old fish
D) Decomposing beavers

On top of the gangrene, you've gone and caught typhoid. What does your body smell of?

A) Fresh bread
B) Fresh flowers
C) Horse manure
D) A PE teacher's pants

Everybody starts to go deaf after what age?

A) At birth
B) Age 21
C) Age 10
D) Age 50

067

What did aristocratic women use as toilet paper in the Middle Ages?

- **A)** Bear fur
- **B)** Goose feathers
- **C)** Dog skin
- **D)** Live kittens

068

If you've got Agomphosis, what are your symptoms?

- **A)** Sweaty feet
- **B)** Bloodshot eyes
- **C)** Loose teeth
- **D)** Stinky farts

069

What do the ceruminous glands make?

- **A)** Snot
- **B)** Earwax
- **C)** Flesh
- **D)** Hair

Somewhere in your body there's a strange blue spot. Whereabouts is it?

A) In your armpit
B) In your belly
C) In your brain
D) In your heart

070

What is "rutilism?"

A) Having vampire's teeth
B) Having baby teeth
C) Having red hair
D) Having grey hair

071

Which of these has the most hair on its body?

A) A human being
B) A snake
C) A chimpanzee
D) A snail

072

073

How much do your nails grow in your lifetime?

- **A)** 4in/10cm
- **B)** 10ft/3m
- **C)** 46ft/14m
- **D)** 92ft/28m

074

How often does the body replace brain cells?

- **A)** Every hour
- **B)** Every day
- **C)** Never
- **D)** Every 5 years

075

The Chinese leader Mao Tse Tung didn't take hygiene very seriously. What horrible thing happened to him?

- **A)** A worm crawled up his behind
- **B)** Maggots ate his eyeballs
- **C)** His teeth turned green
- **D)** His fingers fell off

Where does the Jigger flea like to lay its eggs?

    A) In your brain
    B) In your hair
    C) In your bed
    D) Between your toes

How do surgeons join together small blood vessels that have become detached?

    A) They heat them until they melt and then weld them together
    B) They knot them together with spit
    C) They glue them together with mucus
    D) They sew them with a microscopic needle

If you add together all the time you spend blinking, for how long in a waking day are your eyes actually closed?

    A) 2 minutes
    B) 2 hours
    C) Half an hour
    D) 6 hours

079 **W**hat's unusual about the microbe Thiomargarita namibiensis?

- **A)** It glows
- **B)** It's so small nobody's ever seen one
- **C)** It's so big it's visible to the human eye
- **D)** It eats itself

080 **I**f your poop were "olid" what would it be?

- **A)** Bright blue
- **B)** Incredibly runny
- **C)** Incredibly crumbly
- **D)** Incredibly stinky

081 **A**t what speed is snot moved from the nose and the throat towards the mouth?

- **A)** 0.04in/0.01cm per hour
- **B)** 0.4in/1cm per hour
- **C)** 0.6in/1.5cm per hour
- **D)** 49ft/15m per hour

What amount of weight can your skeleton take before all your bones start to snap?

A) 5 times its own weight
B) Twice its own weight
C) 10 times its own weight
D) 100 times its own weight

What do white blood cells do?

A) Fight germs
B) Fight with red blood cells
C) Nothing, they just laze about
D) Fight amongst themselves

How did the Roman Emperor Frederick I pop his clogs?

A) Fell asleep in a giant catapult and was accidentally fired into a castle moat
B) Stuck his head into a wasps' nest and was stung to death
C) Tried to eat a crab whole and choked to death
D) Jumped into a river with a suit of armor on and drowned

085

How much does an average person pee in a lifetime?

    A) 211 quarts/200 litres
    B) 42,267 quarts/40,000 litres
    C) 10,566quarts/10,000 litres
    D) 1056 quarts/1,000 litres

086

How many viruses can a sneeze contain?

    A) Up to 6 million
    B) Up to 100
    C) Up to 900
    D) None

087

Which of these is a disease that makes your face swell up?

    A) Bumps
    B) Lumps
    C) Dumps
    D) Mumps

What's pus made of?

    A) Dead skin and snot
    B) Dead blood cells and dead bacteria
    C) Bile and blood
    D) Blood and custard

Which of these is the name of a substance your body manufactures to stop viruses from multiplying?

    A) Intercalary
    B) Interferon
    C) Intermezzo
    D) Intertoto

"Yersina pestis" is another name for what?

    A) Runny poop
    B) Hair lice
    C) Plague
    D) Spots

When the Egyptians mummified somebody, how did they remove the person's brain?

- **A)** Drilled a hole in the person's head then sucked it out with a straw
- **B)** Sawed the top of the person's skull
- **C)** Pushed burning leaves in the person's ear to melt it
- **D)** Pulled it out through the person's nose

What causes the disease "Typhus?"

- **A)** Slobbering dogs
- **B)** Pooping lice
- **C)** Peeing cats
- **D)** Sneezing mice

Only one of the following cannot be eaten by any kind of bacteria. Which one?

- **A)** Tarmac
- **B)** Steel
- **C)** Disinfectant
- **D)** Diamonds

What is "naupathia"?

    A) The desire to drink human blood

    B) Sleepiness

    C) The inability to poop

    D) Seasickness

The landlord of a bar in the Yukon, Canada, offered every customer a free drink, yet very few of them accepted What was the drink on offer?

    A) Coca-Cola with a human eyeball in it

    B) Champagne with a human toe in it

    C) Orange squash with a shrunken head in it

    D) Beer with a live frog in it

Dengue fever is also known as what?

    A) Snapskull fever

    B) Brainboil fever

    C) Burnbottom fever

    D) Breakbone fever

097

What product used to be sold to leather workers in the Middle Ages?
- **A)** Sun-dried puke
- **B)** Old pee
- **C)** Hanged men's heads
- **D)** Human skin

098

What happens to astronauts' pee?
- **A)** It's used as fuel
- **B)** It's stored in potties
- **C)** It's dumped in space
- **D)** They're not allowed to pee

099

What is a "xyster"?
- **A)** A person who has a fish's head
- **B)** A type of tapeworm
- **C)** A type of rash
- **D)** A surgeon's instrument for scraping bones

How many people get gobbled up by sharks each year?

- **A)** Between 10 and 12
- **B)** About 6000
- **C)** Between 40 and 50
- **D)** Between 1 and 2

100

How many pairs of muscles are there in the eye?

- **A)** 12
- **B)** 2
- **C)** 1
- **D)** 3

101

What does BCG stand for?

- **A)** Bacillus of Calmette and Guerin
- **B)** Bacillus of Camel and Guava
- **C)** Bi-Cranimial Gilopsican
- **D)** Bleeding Cruel Gash

102

How many miles of capillaries are there in the human body?

 A) 2
 B) 600
 C) 60,000
 D) 60 million

What feat was first achieved in June 1981?

 A) First successful brain transplant
 B) First successful heart bypass operation
 C) First successful reattachment of a severed hand
 D) First successful birth of test-tube twins

Two ingredients of bad breath are hydrogen sulfide and methyl mercaptan. What do they smell of?

 A) Dead fish and old socks
 B) Rotten eggs and skunk oil
 C) Rotten fish and onions
 D) Rotten flesh and cat pee

How many different chemicals help blood become a scab?

    A) 16
    B) 83
    C) 31
    D) 4

What do you do when you basiate?

    A) Fart
    B) Kiss
    C) Burp
    D) Snore

If a doctor told you you were going to have a "barium meal," what would you be in line for?

    A) Boiled cabbage
    B) A vitamin pill
    C) A stomach examination
    D) A brain operation

109

Which of these is so similar to human bone that it's been used in operations to replace bone grafts?

A) Coral
B) Shark bones
C) Monkey bones
D) Concrete

110

How much brain juice does the body make every day for the brain to float about in?

A) About a bucket full
B) About 2 glasses full
C) About half a glass full
D) About a bowl full

111

How far does the average person walk in a lifetime?

A) From Boston to Los Angeles and back
B) From England to Spain and back
C) From Earth to the moon and back
D) From England to Japan and back

Which of these organs can regrow after part of it has been cut away?

- **A)** The brain
- **B)** The kidneys
- **C)** The heart
- **D)** The liver

Bacteria feeding on dead bodies can make the bodies do what?

- **A)** Spontaneously catch fire
- **B)** Move their lips as if they were talking
- **C)** Swell up with methane gas to three times their normal size
- **D)** Shrink to the size of a golf ball

Urea is the substance that makes pee yellow. Where else in the body is it found?

- **A)** The hair
- **B)** The skin
- **C)** The fingernails
- **D)** All of the above

115

Which of these statements is NOT true?
- **A)** You eat an entire cabbage every day
- **B)** You eat tiny parts of other people every day
- **C)** You eat tiny parts of the moon every day
- **D)** You eat tiny parts of yourself every day

116

How many old red blood cells does your body destroy every second?
- **A)** 10
- **B)** 1000
- **C)** 1 million
- **D)** 2 million

117

What do your taste buds look like?
- **A)** Tiny toadstools
- **B)** Curly worms
- **C)** Shiny pools of slime
- **D)** Moldy sausages

If you catch "Blackwater fever" what happens to you?

118

A) Your eyeballs liquefy
B) Your poop turns green
C) Your skin turns scaly
D) Your pee turns red

What did Tudor doctors suggest doing to cure asthma?

119

A) Swallowing frogs
B) Gargling with slugs
C) Licking snails
D) Rubbing your chest with a toad

How many sweat glands are there in the body?

120

A) 2 million
B) 1000
C) 6
D) 2

121 How many different smells can we detect?
A) 1 million
B) 10,000
C) 100
D) 50

122 How many bacteria live on the human skin?

A) About the same number as the number of people who live on your street
B) About the same number as the number of people who live in Britain
C) About the same number as the number of people who live in the world
D) About the same number as the number of people who live in America

123 What are "cilia?"
A) Tiny pulsating hairs on bacteria
B) Tiny spines on germs
C) Blobs of acidic slime in your gut
D) Clouds of gas in your behind

What do "osteoblast" cells do?

124

- **A)** Destroy bones
- **B)** Blow up germs
- **C)** Build up bones
- **D)** Make you sneeze

How much does an adult heart weigh?

125

- **A)** 62 pounds/28kg
- **B)** 6 pounds/2.8g
- **C)** 1 ounce/28g
- **D)** 10 ounces/280g

What happens when you get a bruise?

126

- **A)** Moldy flesh decays under your skin
- **B)** Bone is splintered under your skin
- **C)** Blood vessels burst under your skin
- **D)** A blob of gristle forms under your skin

127

Why are your lips a different color to the rest of your face?

A) Because they contain a special type of blood

B) Because they're really part of your throat, not your face

C) Because they don't have any blood vessels in them

D) Because your spit wears the top layer away

128

How many tons of food will your digestive system turn into fuel and poop in your lifetime?

A) 2

B) 20

C) 50

D) 80

129

On average, how many hairs fall out of your head every day?

A) 800

B) 80

C) 8000

D) 8

Which of these statements is TRUE?

130

A) We all have tiny teeth in our ears
B) We all have tiny horns on our heads
C) We all have tiny wings on our backs
D) We all have a tiny tail on our butts

How much does the lightest bone in the human body weigh?

131

A) About as much as a speck of dust
B) About as much as a postage stamp
C) About as much as a slug
D) About as much as a chocolate bar

In your whole life you will fart enough methane to fly how many hot air balloons?

132

A) 10
B) 5
C) 2
D) 1

133

When you hop on one leg, your ankle bears the force of how many times your body weight?

A) 10 times your body weight
B) 5 times your body weight
C) Twice your body weight
D) 100 times your body weight

134

Bacteria were responsible for something terrible happening at the funeral of King George V's brother-in-law. What was it?

A) The corpse turned runny and leaked out of the coffin
B) The corpse smelt so bad many of the mourners fainted
C) The corpse exploded
D) The corpse started groaning and they had to cancel the funeral

135

Pound for pound, human bone is how much stronger than steel?

A) Twice as strong
B) 5 times as strong
C) 10 times as strong
D) 100 times as strong

What is a "trepan?"

A) A kind of Hoover used to clean out people's butts

B) A kind of potato-peeler used to peel people's skin

C) A kind of scoop used to take out people's eyes

D) A kind of saw used to open people's skulls

What did "gong scourers" do in the Middle Ages?

A) Wipe the bottoms of rich people

B) Shovel poop from rich people's homes

C) Clean rich people's gongs

D) Take the blame when a rich person farted

How often, on average, do people fart each day?

A) Once or twice

B) 6 times

C) 31 times

D) 13 times

139 In 40 years' time, what size will your ears be?

- **A)** They'll still be the same size as they are now
- **B)** They'll be about 2.8in/7cm bigger
- **C)** They'll be about 0.3in/0.7cm bigger
- **D)** They'll be about 5.5in/14cm smaller

140 How long does it take your kidneys to clean and filter all of the blood in your body?

- **A)** About a week
- **B)** About half an hour
- **C)** About 2 days
- **D)** About 2 hours

141 How much oil can the skin secrete in a month?

- **A)** Enough to fill a mug
- **B)** Enough to fill a bucket
- **C)** Enough to fill a swimming pool
- **D)** Enough to fill a bath

Where does the eight-legged demodex mite like to live?

- **A)** In your eyebrows
- **B)** Under your fingernails
- **C)** Behind your ears
- **D)** In your armpits

Where would you find "endoplasmic reticulum?"

- **A)** In your behind
- **B)** Inside bones
- **C)** Inside cells
- **D)** On the surface of the tongue

A lot of your body is being replaced every day without you noticing. How old do you think most of a 100-year-old person's body is?

- **A)** Less than a year old
- **B)** Less than 10 years old
- **C)** Less than 50 years old
- **D)** 100 years old

145 **A**n average poop is what % water?

A) 5%
B) 25%
C) 50%
D) 75%

146 **W**hat does "pandiculation" refer to?

A) Sleepwalking
B) Wetting the bed
C) Yawning
D) Having bad breath

147 **I**n the time of Henry VIII, what happened to people who were found guilty of poisoning someone?

A) They had their guts pulled out
B) They were boiled alive
C) They had their noses cut off
D) They had their tongues cut out

Which is the longest nerve in the body?

- **A)** Aquatic nerve
- **B)** Sciatic nerve
- **C)** Static nerve
- **D)** Ugotta nerve

If you lose the blood supply to your brain, how long would it take for you to fall unconscious?

- **A)** About 3 weeks
- **B)** About a minute
- **C)** About 10 seconds
- **D)** 0.03 seconds

Which of these are contained in most chocolate bars?

- **A)** Insect fragments
- **B)** Rat hairs
- **C)** Shell fragments
- **D)** All of the above

151 What's the deepest anyone's ever gone underwater without using a breathing device (and without drowning)?

- **A)** 13 metres/42.5 feet
- **B)** 38 metres/124.5 feet
- **C)** 67 metres/220 feet
- **D)** 86 metres/282 feet

152 Who's more likely to end up getting toasted by lightning?

- **A)** Adult women
- **B)** Adult men
- **C)** Children
- **D)** All have the same chance

153 Which of these is true?

- **A)** Your left leg is slightly thicker than your right leg
- **B)** Your left eyeball is slightly smaller than your right eyeball
- **C)** Your left nostril makes tastier snot than your right nostril
- **D)** Your left lung breathes in slightly less air than your right lung

Roughly how many nerve endings are there per square inch in your hand?

A) 1,300
B) 750
C) 1000
D) 10

154

What did Tudor doctors suggest doing if you were bald?

A) Rubbing crushed slugs on your head
B) Eating live snails
C) Eating live crows
D) Rubbing crushed beetles on your head

155

What do "glucocorticoids" do?

A) Prevent bleeding
B) Prevent infection
C) Prevent swelling
D) Prevent you doing your homework

156

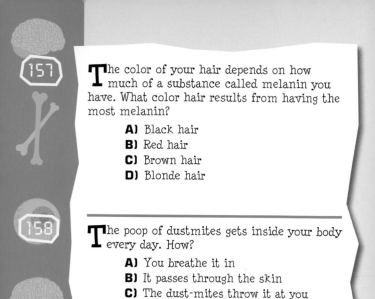

157

The color of your hair depends on how much of a substance called melanin you have. What color hair results from having the most melanin?

- **A)** Black hair
- **B)** Red hair
- **C)** Brown hair
- **D)** Blonde hair

158

The poop of dustmites gets inside your body every day. How?

- **A)** You breathe it in
- **B)** It passes through the skin
- **C)** The dust-mites throw it at you
- **D)** It jumps off your hand when you scratch your behind

159

How many glands in your ear canal produce wax?

- **A)** 50,000
- **B)** 2,000
- **C)** 100
- **D)** None

What does "formication" describe?

   A) A feeling like ants crawling on your skin
   B) A feeling like tiny hammers bashing your teeth
   C) A feeling like peeing fire
   D) A feeling like tiny pins jabbing your eyes

160

How many hairs are there on a normal human body?

   A) 5000
   B) 50,000
   C) 5 million
   D) 50 million

161

Which of these can you not get an artificial replacement for?

   A) Jaw
   B) Cortex
   C) Larynx
   D) Shoulder

162

163 **W**hich of these facts is true?

A) Your brain uses 13% more energy watching television than doing nothing

B) Your brain uses 26% more energy doing puzzles than doing nothing

C) Your brain uses 13% less energy watching television than doing nothing

D) Your brain uses 26% less energy doing puzzles than doing nothing

164 **W**hat did the ancient Egyptians use to make false eyes for their mummies?

A) Eggs

B) Onions

C) Seashells

D) Rocks

165 **H**ow many tiny droplets of spit do we all spray when we're talking?

A) About 3 a minute

B) About 30 a minute

C) About 300 a minute

D) About 3000 a minute

Which is heavier: the spleen, the liver or the kidneys?

- **A)** The spleen
- **B)** The kidneys
- **C)** The liver
- **D)** All weigh exactly the same

If you're "nauseous" what are you most likely to do?

- **A)** Puke
- **B)** Pee in your bed
- **C)** Sneeze
- **D)** Poop in your pants

If you catch the "ebola virus", you're likely to start bleeding from where?

- **A)** The ears
- **B)** The behind
- **C)** The eyeballs
- **D)** All three

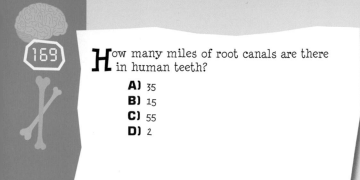

169

How many miles of root canals are there in human teeth?

- **A)** 35
- **B)** 15
- **C)** 55
- **D)** 2

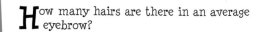

170

How many hairs are there in an average eyebrow?

- **A)** About 50
- **B)** About 100
- **C)** About 500
- **D)** About 5000

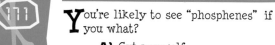

171

You're likely to see "phosphenes" if you what?

- **A)** Cut yourself
- **B)** Go into space
- **C)** Pick your nose
- **D)** Rub your eyes

Hypertrophy of the tongue would mean what?

A) Your tongue had swelled up so that it was too big to fit back in your mouth

B) Your tongue was forked like a snake's

C) You'd swallowed your tongue

D) Your tongue had gone a moldy green color

What color is the spleen?

A) Yellowish

B) Greyish

C) Purplish

D) It's see-through

The brain is full of tiny neurons which are needed to make sense of what the various parts of your body are doing. How many of them die in your brain every day?

A) 10

B) 1000

C) 85,000

D) 250,000

175 **W**hat were children in the 17th century sometimes beaten by their teachers for NOT doing?

    A) Not farting

    B) Not spitting

    C) Not burping

    D) Not smoking

176 **W**hich of these do tears NOT contain?

    A) Ammonia

    B) Citric acid

    C) Sulfuric acid

    D) Sugar

177 **W**hy do the skin flakes of men have five times more germs than the skin flakes from women?

    A) Men wash less

    B) Men sweat more

    C) Men wash more

    D) Germs like men better

How long would it take a bacterium to swim one mile?

178

- **A)** Six weeks
- **B)** A week
- **C)** A day
- **D)** Half an hour

Where in the body would you find "otoliths?"

179

- **A)** In the armpits
- **B)** In the brain
- **C)** In the mouth
- **D)** In the ear

When a severed finger is sewn back on, surgeons sometimes do what?

180

- **A)** Hit the finger with a hammer to try and help the blood flow
- **B)** Put a blood-sucking leech on the finger to help the blood flow
- **C)** Hang the patient upside down to help the blood flow
- **D)** Do a special dance to help the blood flow

181 **E**very drop of blood in your body must be replenished with oxygen how often?

  A) Once a minute
  B) Once an hour
  C) Once a day
  D) Every Christmas

182 **H**ow big can a tapeworm grow inside a human belly?

  A) 6 inches
  B) 2 feet
  C) 10 feet
  D) 30 feet

183 **W**hat area of the body does the word "mammila" refer to?

  A) Armpits
  B) Nipples
  C) Nostrils
  D) Skull

Black puke is a pretty good sign you've caught what disease?

- **A)** Black fever
- **B)** Yellow fever
- **C)** Hayfever
- **D)** Saturday night fever

What are "fontanels?"

- **A)** Hairy warts
- **B)** Bits of gristle in between bones
- **C)** Squishy parts of babies' skulls
- **D)** Itchy scabs

What did "night-soil" men do in the 1700s?

- **A)** Buried victims of the plague
- **B)** Robbed corpses of their gold teeth
- **C)** Dug up corpses to sell to doctors
- **D)** Collected poop from huge poop-pools

187 Which of these is true: Human beings have . . . . ?

- **A)** The same number of teeth as a shark
- **B)** The same number of neck bones as a giraffe
- **C)** The same number of brain cells as a dinosaur
- **D)** The same number of scales as a snake

---

188 What's the hardest substance made by the human body?

- **A)** Knuckles
- **B)** Forehead bone
- **C)** Fingernails
- **D)** Tooth enamel

---

189 Your intestines are full of small cactus-like things called villi. What do they do?

- **A)** Squirt acid to break down food
- **B)** Fight bacteria that might be in your food
- **C)** Pack waste products together into sausage shapes
- **D)** Absorb nutrients into your blood

A pneumatic drill makes a sound of 70 decibels. How loud can snores be?

- **A)** 10 decibels
- **B)** 70 decibels
- **C)** 100 decibels
- **D)** 200 decibels

Which of these is true?

- **A)** Your poop is about twice the size as whatever you eat
- **B)** Your poop is about half the size of whatever you eat
- **C)** Your poop is about the same size as whatever you eat
- **D)** Your poop is about a third of the size of whatever you eat

---

The poison from a pufferfish can have what effect on you?

- **A)** Turn you into a very old person in a week
- **B)** Turn you into a zombie
- **C)** Cause your flesh to dissolve until you're a human skeleton
- **D)** Make hair sprout all over your body like a werewolf

193

What percentage of the brain is fat?

A) 1%
B) 50%
C) 10%
D) 99%

194

How many messages are sent to your brain every hour?

A) 47
B) 12,000
C) 9 million
D) 360 trillion

195

What's the total length of all the blood vessels in your body?

A) 100,000 miles/160,930 km
B) 1000 miles/1609 km
C) 1 mile/1.6 km
D) 1 million miles/1,609,300 km

What is "cerumen?"

- **A)** Snot
- **B)** The pigment that makes poop brown
- **C)** Pus
- **D)** Earwax

What makes some hair curly?

- **A)** The hair grows out of oval shaped follicles
- **B)** The hair grows out of curly shaped follicles
- **C)** Special curly blood cells
- **D)** The hair grows out of follicles that are spinning

What did "dredgermen" do in Victorian times?

- **A)** Sifted sewage looking for lost jewelry
- **B)** Emptied giant pits of poop
- **C)** Fished dead bodies out of rivers
- **D)** Arrested people who smelt out toilets

The normal force of gravity is known as 1 "G." You would die after one minute if you were exposed to how many "Gs"?

    A) 2
    B) 250
    C) 100
    D) 10

The ulnar nerve is associated with what sensation?

    A) Getting a migraine
    B) Banging your funny bone
    C) Needing to go to the bathroom
    D) Feeling dizzy

How much of the brain is water?

    A) 85%
    B) 75%
    C) 50%
    D) 12%

How many pain sensors are there in the brain?

- **A)** 12
- **B)** None
- **C)** 768
- **D)** Too many to count

What do schoolboys in Morocco eat to help improve their memories?

- **A)** Asparagus
- **B)** Spinach
- **C)** Hedgehog livers
- **D)** Monkey brains

When Albert Einstein died, his brain was put where?

- **A)** In a jar
- **B)** In a robot
- **C)** In a coffin
- **D)** In a trashcan

205 What part of the brain controls conscious thought?

    A) Brain stem
    B) Hypothalamus
    C) Forebrain
    D) Think tank

206 What part of the brain controls temperature?

    A) Thermostatus
    B) Right hemisphere
    C) Corpus callosum
    D) Hypothalamus

207 Up to what percentage of all oxygen coming into the body can the brain use?

    A) 100
    B) 7
    C) 15
    D) 20

How many hemispheres are there in the brain?

    A) 8

    B) 4

    C) 2

    D) 1

208

How much does the brain weigh?

    A) 14lbs or more

    B) 7lbs

    C) 8lbs

    D) 3lbs or less

209

What does the brain stem do?

    A) Deals with basic life functions, e.g. breathing

    B) Controls hunger

    C) Sorts out right from wrong

    D) Controls temperature

210

211 When a baby is born, how many brain cells does it start off with?

- **A)** 2
- **B)** 47
- **C)** 1 million
- **D)** Over a trillion

212 What part makes sure that signals get through to the body from the brain?

- **A)** Thalamus
- **B)** Midbrain
- **C)** Left hemisphere
- **D)** Modem

213 Where is gray matter located?

- **A)** In your armpits
- **B)** Brain stem
- **C)** Between the black and white matter
- **D)** Cerebral cortex

Which brain part controls behavior?

- **A)** Limbic system
- **B)** Disassociative lobe
- **C)** Parental cortex
- **D)** Humerus

How much of the body is water?

- **A)** Two thirds
- **B)** One third
- **C)** One half
- **D)** One quarter

You would lose the ability to walk after losing what percentage of water from your body ?

- **A)** 5
- **B)** 10
- **C)** 20
- **D)** 25

217

What are the smallest blood vessels
called?

  A) Busta
  B) Veins
  C) Capillaries
  D) Arteries

218

Which veins take the blood from the brain
to the heart?

  A) Jugular
  B) Neural
  C) Cardiac
  D) Pulmonary

219

Which of the following is NOT a part of
the heart?

  A) Right ventricle
  B) Left atrium
  C) Stake
  D) Aorta

What artificial part can be fitted to regulate your heartbeat?

A) Automaton
B) Stopwatch
C) Electrocardiogram
D) Pacemaker

How many barrels of blood are pumped round the body in an average lifetime?

A) 42
B) 1000
C) 1,000,000
D) 10,000,000

What term is given to a photograph of the inside of your body

A) Molaroid
B) X-ray
C) Innermatic
D) Lasermatic

223 **W**hich of the following does NOT stain your teeth?

    A) Antibiotics
    B) Coffee
    C) Lemons
    D) Smoking

224 **W**hich of the following have the most bacteria in their teeth?

    A) Dogs
    B) Humans
    C) Combs
    D) Worms

225 **W**hat causes bad breath?

    A) Sucking your thumb
    B) Fillings
    C) Eating apples
    D) Decaying food stuck in teeth

How many permanent teeth does an adult have?

A) 40
B) 32
C) 24
D) 12

226

What is the rock-hard substance covering the tooth called?

A) Dentin
B) Enamel
C) Granite
D) Cementum

227

What are the cutting teeth called?

A) Incisors
B) Fangs
C) Molars
D) Cutters

228

229

What are the grinding teeth at the back of the mouth called?

A) Pestles

B) Incisors

C) Molars

D) Mortars

230

Do wisdom teeth increase brain power?

A) Yes, because they carry memory cells

B) No

C) Yes, because they help control pain

D) Yes, because they cause puberty

231

Approximately how much of the population is left-handed?

A) 85

B) 25

C) 50

D) 10

Which of the following do NOT contain keratin?

    A) Zits
    B) Tears
    C) Nails
    D) Hair

If you stick something in your ears, doctors recommend it should be no smaller than a what?

    A) Q-Tip
    B) Pencil
    C) Finger
    D) Elbow

What is the average temperature of a human being?

    A) 32°F/0°C
    B) 96.8°F/36°C
    C) 98.6°F/37°C
    D) 101°F/38°C

235 Why do you wrinkle in the bath?

A) Moisture is being sucked out of your body into the bath

B) Dead skin cells plump up in the warm water so they don't lie flat anymore

C) Skin falls off leaving new wrinkly skin exposed

D) It is a trick of the light due to water refraction

236 What is neurapraxia better known as

A) Heatstroke

B) Earache

C) Diarrhea

D) Pins and needles

237 When a baby is born, what connects it to its mother?

A) Umbilical cord

B) Handcuffs

C) Fallopian tube

D) Apron string

Humans have the remnants of a tail –
what's it called?

- **A)** Medulla oblongata
- **B)** Sternum
- **C)** Coccyx
- **D)** Don't be silly – humans don't have a tail

How many sets of ribs do you have?

- **A)** 14
- **B)** 12
- **C)** 6
- **D)** 12 in women, 11 in men

How much of your weight do your big toes bear?

- **A)** None
- **B)** One half
- **C)** Two thirds
- **D)** One quarter

241

How many bones does an adult have?
- **A)** 166
- **B)** 186
- **C)** 206
- **D)** Over 300

242

How many bones are babies born with?
- **A)** 166
- **B)** Over 300
- **C)** 250
- **D)** 206

243

How many flakes of skin do you shed every minute?
- **A)** 500
- **B)** 50,000
- **C)** 5,000
- **D)** 50

What does an appendix do?

A) Helps you digest meat
B) Helps you digest salad
C) Nothing
D) Controls the color of poop

Which muscle never rests

A) Bicep
B) Pectoral
C) Lungs
D) Heart

What part of the body, especially on sleeping campers, has been most attacked by vampire bats?

A) Fingers
B) Neck
C) Ears
D) Big toe

Record-breaking Allen Doster donated how many pints of blood between 1966 and 1986?

- **A)** 1092
- **B)** 1800
- **C)** 546
- **D)** 25,000

On average, how many times will your heart beat in a lifetime?

- **A)** 1 million
- **B)** 62 million
- **C)** 98 billion
- **D)** 1 billion

How often should you clean your teeth to keep them healthy?

- **A)** Twice a day
- **B)** Twice a week
- **C)** Once a week
- **D)** It doesn't matter as long as you don't eat sweets

The word skeleton comes from ancient Greek. What does it mean?

    A) White
    B) Frame
    C) Scary monster
    D) Dried up

What is the largest organ inside the body?

    A) Barrel
    B) Liver
    C) Heart
    D) Church

What color are bones in the body?

    A) Beige/Light Brown
    B) White
    C) Orange
    D) Black

253 Which of the following functions does a skeleton not have?

- **A)** Feels pain
- **B)** Makes blood cells
- **C)** Provides for muscle attachment
- **D)** Protects internal organs

254 The skeleton also stores what?

- **A)** Insulin
- **B)** Minerals
- **C)** Gelatin
- **D)** Hormones

255 How many pints of tears do your eyes produce in one year?

- **A)** 8
- **B)** 6
- **C)** 4
- **D)** 2

Which of the following CANNOT cause hiccups?

  A) Drinking fizzy drinks
  B) Eating quickly
  C) Being scared
  D) Chewing gum

256

How many bacteria are there on an average face?

  A) 2000
  B) 2 million
  C) 1 billion
  D) 68,000

257

What is the most contagious disease?

  A) Legionnaire's disease
  B) Ecoli
  C) Common cold
  D) Gastro-enteritis

258

259

How many smell cells do we have?
- **A)** 1000
- **B)** 5 million
- **C)** 100,000
- **D)** 50,000

260

Which of the following smells does a human body NOT emit?
- **A)** Acetic acid (vinegar)
- **B)** Hydrogen sulfide (rotten eggs)
- **C)** Eucalyptus (medicinal antiseptic)
- **D)** Mercaptans (skunk smell)

261

The nastiest smell that we give off is called seleno mercaptan. What is it said to smell like?
- **A)** A mixture of antiseptic and rubber
- **B)** A mixture of glue and vomit
- **C)** A mixture of onion, sewage, rotting cabbage and garlic
- **D)** A mixture of horse manure and vinegar

Which of these IS a part of the body

A) Crown
B) Elementary canal
C) Mussels
D) The humorous

At what speed does sound travel through the air to your ear?

A) 1837m/2956km per second
B) 1166m/1876km per second
C) 701m/1229km per second
D) 148m/238 km per second

How much poop does each person produce in a year, on average?

A) 10 pounds
B) 50 pounds
C) 1.5 tons
D) 5 tons

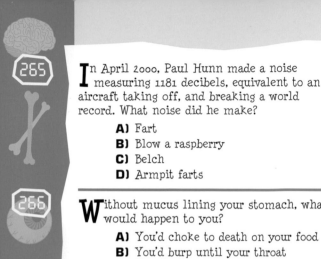

265 In April 2000, Paul Hunn made a noise measuring 118.1 decibels, equivalent to an aircraft taking off, and breaking a world record. What noise did he make?

    A) Fart
    B) Blow a raspberry
    C) Belch
    D) Armpit farts

266 Without mucus lining your stomach, what would happen to you?

    A) You'd choke to death on your food
    B) You'd burp until your throat dissolved
    C) You'd drown in your own blood
    D) You'd digest your own stomach

267 What are those specks and floaters in your eyes?

    A) Shadows of shriveled bits of protein and old blood vessels that have been trapped in your eyes since before you were born
    B) Stray eyelashes
    C) Dust
    D) You're actually seeing reflections of the brain's electrical impulses

Rods and Cones are the cells in the eyes that respond to light and color, but which is which?

A) Rods allow you to see black, white and blue. Cones provide the red and green

B) Cones allow you to see in black and white in dim light. Rods provide the color in bright light

C) Rods allow you to see in black and white in dim light. Cones provide the color in bright light

D) Cones allow you to see red and green. Rods provide the black, white and blue

---

What is hemophobia the fear of?

A) Snot
B) Pee
C) Blood
D) Poop

Which of these features are unique?

A) Fingerprints
B) Iris
C) Ear prints
D) All of the above

Other Titles

There are many other exciting quiz
and puzzle books in the IntelliQuest range,
and your QUIZMO electronic unit
knows the answers to them all!

You can order from your local
IntelliQuest stockist or on-line bookseller.

For a full listing of current titles
(and ISBN numbers) see:

www.intelliquestbooks.com

LAGOON
BOOKS